THE NATURE OF PSYCH

THE NATURE OF PSYCHOTHERAPY

A CRITICAL APPRAISAL

KARL JASPERS

TRANSLATED BY

J. HOENIG & MARIAN W. HAMILTON

PHOENIX BOOKS
THE UNIVERSITY OF CHICAGO PRESS

This book is an extract from *General Psychopathology*, published 1963 by the University of Chicago Press and Manchester University Press, a translation of the seventh edition (1959) of *Allgemeine Pathologie*, originally published 1913.

The University of Chicago Press, Chicago 60637

Manchester University Press, Manchester 13, England
The University of Toronto Press, Toronto 5, Canada

FOREWORD

by Sir Aubrey Lewis, F.R.C.P.

Professor of Psychiatry, University of London

PSYCHIATRY abounds in moot points and controversial issues: and of all the branches of psychiatry none is richer in these than psychotherapy. Its aims, its essence, its methods, its mode of action, its efficiency: these are all subjects of lively contention. Anyone who enters into the disputes is likely to be a partisan. It is fortunate therefore that the one contemporary philosopher who has an unrivalled acquaintance with the basic problems of psychiatry has turned his dispassionate attention to the theme of psychotherapy. In this little book, extracted from his magistral exposition *General Psychopathology*, Karl Jaspers surveys the field with judicious interest. His comments, because they are in general terms and calmly stated, seem simple, and at times self-evident: but more closely examined they are seen not only to run counter to many currently accepted ideas, but also to contain penetrating criticisms and some illuminating statements about the scope and goals of psychotherapy. Psychiatry in Germany and Switzerland, the countries in which Professor Jaspers has gained his experience of it, differs in some ways from psychiatry in the English-speaking countries: the differences are evident here, and there are some matters, such as his views on non-medical psychotherapists, which are unlikely to pass without challenge. But all psychiatrists—even those who contest Professor Jaspers' views—will readily acknowledge the stimulus derived from finding the large issues of psychotherapy considered with such detached yet acute scrutiny.

AUTHOR'S PREFACE

IN these days psychotherapy has become nearly everyone's concern. Although it arose within the field of Medicine, it has now detached itself from this source. At the present time we find psychotherapists, who have no medical training, as well as medical psychotherapists, whose medical training is rarely brought to bear on their work. Anyone who intends to undergo psychotherapy should know what he is doing and what he is to expect.

In this small volume I have reproduced two sections from my own *General Psychopathology*. These sections deal explicitly with psychotherapy. They seem to me well suited for anyone who takes an interest in these questions, and who is looking for some information. They can be readily understood by all, but within the framework of the larger volume they are not easily accessible to the wider public.

I would like the book to be of use to all who are ready to look at the subject reasonably, think about it and develop some critical attitude of their own towards it.

KARL JASPERS

TRANSLATORS' INTRODUCTION

PROFESSOR Jaspers was one of a number of brilliant psychiatrists, among them Mayer-Gross, Gruhle and Homburger,
who were united under the leadership of Professor F. Nissl. This
group of workers became known as the 'Heidelberg School' and as
such exerted an influence far beyond that of any school psychiatry.
Jaspers' particular contribution was his famous and fundamental
book *General Psychopathology* which, ever since its publication in
1913, has been a basic textbook for psychiatry as a whole. The fact
that by 1959 it had run into seven editions bears witness to the
steady increase of its continuing influence. Working from the
7th edition, we have translated this great book into English and
it was published by Manchester University Press in the Spring of
1963.

Since 'The Nature of Psychotherapy' is an excerpt from this
book, it is now therefore available to English readers, but, like
Professor Jaspers himself, we think it well worth while bringing out
this small volume separately, as the subject of psychotherapy is of
enormous interest to a far wider public than have the time or equipment to read the larger and more specialized work.

Many people are bewildered by the confusing number of psychotherapeutic approaches. Only recently a book appeared describing
the '36 most important schools of psycho-analysis in the United
States'. If this is the number only of the *most important* schools and
only of the *psychoanalytic* ones, that is, excluding all the many
other camps of psychology, and only of those *within the United
States*, one can only dimly conjecture how many schools of psychotherapy there may be altogether. There seems a definite need for
some fresh appraisal of general principles.

As Sir Aubrey points out there is no-one better suited and
qualified to discuss such topics than Karl Jaspers, who is equally
versed in clinical psychiatry *and* philosophy. His eminence in psychiatry is established once and for all by his *General Psychopathology*.
As a philosopher he hardly needs introduction. He held the Chair
in Philosophy at Heidelberg University from 1921 to 1948, when

he was called to the Chair in Basle, Switzerland, where he still is. Among his philosophical writings *Die Psychologie der Weltanschauungen* ('The psychology of philosophies')[1] and *Die Geistige Situation der Zeit* ('Man in the modern Age')[2] are of more than ordinary importance for psychiatry. His tenure of the Heidelberg Chair was interrupted from 1936 to 1945 when he was deposed by the German Government of the day who forbade him to teach on political and other grounds. During these nine years, with their hardships of existence for an antagonist of the Government, Karl Jaspers wrote his very much enlarged 4th edition of *General Psychopathology* which appeared in 1946 and remained unchanged in all the subsequent editions.

In the following critique of psychotherapy Professor Jaspers applies the same analysis of method and the same philosophical criteria as he applies to psychiatry as a whole. Those unfamiliar with his thought in this respect should refer to his major work. For a brief and useful statement of his main philosophical ideas, the reader may refer to H. J. Blackham's exposition (1956).[3] The terminology is relatively new to British psychotherapeutic literature and the following points are basic to a full understanding of the argument:

The psychopathologist studies the human being from three aspects, each of which commands its own separate methods. Psychological understanding is only one of these whereby the whole vast variety of phenomena can be adequately approached. It has inevitably certain limits. These are set on the one hand by extra-conscious mechanisms belonging to the somatic substrate, which can be studied only by the methods of science, and on the other by the ununderstandability of Existence as such, which transcends our knowledge and which can only be illuminated by intuition. One of Jaspers' main tenets is, therefore, that if justice is to be done to human personality, all three methods of approach must be employed but carefully differentiated, and he finds that psychotherapeutic practice and theory suffer badly from confusion on this score. There is (1) *causal explanation*, linking together several elements

---

[1] 4th edn., J. Springer, Berlin, 1954.
[2] 2nd edn., Routledge, London, 1951 (Translation).
[3] *Six Existentialist Thinkers*, Routledge & Kegan Paul, 1956 (4th impression).

objectively and formulating laws on the basis of *repeated* experience, (2) a *subjective understanding of meaning*, the understanding of psychogenic developments by *empathy* into psychic material and (3) *existential communication*, illumination of the self and the other in the process of living, through unpredictable glimpses of Transcendence, expressed in symbolic action and speech and mutually understood. This intuition of the patient as a whole person with freedom as well as limits is an important guide to the therapist but such intuitions must be clearly differentiated from scientific knowledge which can be predicted and tested. Neither the intuitive nor the scientific approach should be neglected and, if they are not kept separate, hopeless confusion will result.

Jaspers insists on clarity of thought in psychotherapy and such people are often accused of a lack of imagination. But no one can level that criticism against Jaspers. In his earliest clinical writings, such as *Heimweh und Verbrechen*[1] ('Homesickness and Crime') and *Eifersuchtswahn* ('Delusions of Jealousy'),[2] far from offering any threat to intuition and imagination in clinical psychiatry, he is already showing himself as their protector. His pathographies on Strindberg, Van Gogh, Hölderlin and Swedenborg,[3] as well as on Nietzsche,[4] also show him to be a connoisseur of the humanities and perfectly at home with them.

The present argument does not lose itself in technicalities nor in any school psychology but it examines psychotherapy as a single, contemporary phenomenon, examines its setting in our time. As such the book is of great interest to psychotherapists, psychologists, philosophers and the public at large, particularly the growing number of those who have to look to psychotherapy as a source of help for their own illness or disability. This and the whole line of philosophical thought indicated above give the essay its unique flavour and cause the translators to hope that it will commend itself to all its readers.

UNIVERSITY OF MANCHESTER
Department of Psychiatry

J. HOENIG
M. HAMILTON

[1] *Arch. f. Krim. Anthropol*, 1909, 35; 1.
[2] *Z. gesam. Neurol. Psychiat*, 1910, Orig. Vol. 1, pp. 567–637.
[3] *Strindberg & Van Gogh*, R. Piper, München, 1949.
[4] *Nietzsche. Einführung in das Verständnis seines Philosophierens*, 3rd edn., W. Gruyter & Co., Berlin, 1950.

CONTENTS

Page

I. PSYCHOTHERAPY

Methods of suggestion   1

Cathartic methods   2

Methods involving practice and training   2

Methods of re-education   3

Methods that address themselves to personality   3

II. THE MEANING OF MEDICAL PRACTICE IN PSYCHOTHERAPY

The relation of knowledge to practice   8

The contingent nature of all therapy   9

Legal steps, expert opinion and psychotherapy   12

The link with different levels of general medical therapy   14

Types of inner obstacle—the patient's decision to undergo psychotherapy   20

The aims and limits of psychotherapy   23

The personal role of the doctor   27

Different psychiatric attitudes   29

Harmful psychological atmospheres   33

The public aspect of psychotherapy   34

Index   51

I

PSYCHOTHERAPY

PSYCHOTHERAPY is the name given to all those methods of treatment that affect both psyche and body by measures which proceed via the psyche. The co-operation of the patient is always required. Psychotherapy has application to those who suffer from the many types of personality-disorder (psychopathies), also to the mildly psychotic patient, to all people who feel ill and suffer from their psychic state, and almost without exception to physical illnesses, which so often are overlaid with neurotic symptoms and with which the personality must inwardly come to terms. In all these instances we have in our possession the following means of influencing the psyche:

METHODS OF SUGGESTION

Without addressing ourselves to the patient's personality, we use mechanisms of suggestion to obtain certain concrete effects: the removal of particular symptoms, of physical sequelae, the improvement of sleep, etc. We render the patient accessible to suggestion either in the *hypnotic* state or in the *waking* state and we persuade him of what we want to achieve. Everything depends on the vividness and impressiveness of the ideas we can rouse in the patient and on the vitally forceful presence of the suggestor. All this is helped by the patient's faith and given that a good result is rapidly achieved.

Although doctor and patient are not always aware of it, the influence of suggestion is also at work in a large number of medicinal, electro-therapeutic and other measures, which over the ages have attained striking success with psychically and nervously ill people. It is all the same whether one prescribes sugared water, coloured water, tonic pills; whether one actually sends a galvanic current through the body or only pretends to do so with the help of complicated apparatus. The important thing is that the patient should be convinced of the significance of what is done. He must have faith in the power of science or in the skill and knowledge of his doctor, as a person both resolute and authoritative.[1]

CATHARTIC METHODS

In so far as patients suffer from the after-effects of experiences and their particular symptoms are a manifestation of these, the affects (emotions) which are the source of the trouble need to be 'abreacted' in some manner. This kind of psychoanalytic treatment was developed into a method by Breuer and Freud. The later elaborations by Freud need not be accepted in detail, so long as we recognize the underlying principle. That is, we let the patients unburden themselves, direct the conversation when important matters seem concealed, show them understanding and give an assurance that we make no moral judgments about them. 'Confessions' of this sort often bring relief. There are some cases where completely forgotten (dissociated) experiences can be made conscious and where this leads to a direct cessation of an abnormal physical or psychic symptom. Frank has elaborated a method for calling forth forgotten experiences in the course of a hypnotic half-sleep and then abreacting them.

METHODS INVOLVING PRACTICE AND TRAINING

The patient works upon himself regularly and repeatedly, following certain rules. The aim is to achieve indirectly certain changes in psychic attitude that are desired and to help the patient acquire new capacities.

(a) *Exercises:* Physical exercises are used widely nowadays and take many different forms. Unconscious psychic life, unwitting attitudes and inner states can be influenced either by the conscious will—usually with but small effect—or by the performance of certain acts (magic rites, religious and folk ceremonials, etc.). In these modern days of unbelief we attempt to bring about such

[1] During the first World War an old, crude method practised in the Erbs clinic (Heidelberg) became well known. Strong galvanic currents were used for the immediate removal of hysterical phenomena. Kaufmann, 'Die planmässige Heilung komplizierter Bewegungsstörungen bei Soldaten in einer Sitzung', *Münch. med. Woch.*, 1916, I.

changes in the unconscious psychic life by the more matter-of-fact way of physical exercises. By relaxation and release, by bracing or fortifying the body, we change the psyche at the same time.

In the case of the harassed, always active Westerner, who persistently keeps his will-power at the stretch, relaxation exercises are of the greatest importance. Some therapists favour breathing exercises; breathing with its inspiration and expiration acts as a symbol of taking the outer world in and surrendering to it. By a conscious training in breathing it is thought that the unconscious psychic life can be freed enough so as to trust itself to the world.

(b) *Autogenic training:* This was evolved into a method by J. H. Schultz. It implies a deliberate effort of will directed upon one's own psychic and somatic life, through first inducing a change in consciousness and then through auto-suggestion, a state of 'complete inward self-relaxation'.

METHODS OF RE-EDUCATION

The more the patient turns to the doctor to accept his authority and be guided, the more the relationship may assume the character of re-education. The patient is taken out of his usual environment into a hospital, a spa or sanatorium. Within the authoritative atmosphere of an ordered existence, he becomes re-educated. There is a complete regimentation of the patient's life. He must know what he is to do hour by hour and has to stick strictly to his programme.

METHODS THAT ADDRESS THEMSELVES TO PERSONALITY

If responsibility for the therapeutic effect is laid on the patient and final decisions are left to him, if his own discretion remains the measure and he has to take direct action himself, then the method followed is fundamentally different from all the ones mentioned above. It is simpler in form but more significant for the human being than the preceding methods. It is the most difficult to reduce to a few rules and depends to a large extent on tact and sensitivity to nuance.

(a) The doctor *tells the patient what he knows of the psychopathology,* and what exactly is the matter with him. For instance, where a patient understands the phasic character of his cyclothymia, this helps him to get rid of unfounded fears and comprehend the extra-conscious causes of the various phenomena, which perhaps have been troubling him on moral grounds.

(*b*) The doctor *wants to reason and convince* and works on the value-judgments and general outlook of the patient. We speak here of methods of persuasion.

(*c*) The doctor *addresses himself to the will-power*. In the one case he fosters an effort of will, in another the rejection of some misplaced self-discipline. It is of decisive importance for him to distinguish those phenomena which are to a certain extent accessible to the patient's self-control from those which are not (compulsive phenomena, for example). To the careful, critical observer it is often uncertain at what point the patient's will can or should take a hold and where, in another case, such an effort is only likely to make things worse and what is needed is relaxation.

We know our conscious life is, as it were, only the topmost layer of a wide and deep realm of sub-conscious and extra-conscious events. Self-education lies in influencing this sub-conscious, psychic life, directing its effects, giving them free rein or inhibiting them. Contrasting methods are required depending on the kind of psychic life. On the one hand, in the face of inhibition and conventional influences, it is necessary to encourage surrender to the unconscious, ability to wait, a capacity to listen to the voice of instinct and feeling; slumbering elements in the unconscious need to be aroused. On the other hand, we have to train the will-power to inhibit and suppress when certain areas of the unconscious have grown at the expense of others and thrown the patient off his balance. Thus on the one hand the doctor's influence encourages activity and effort and on the other relaxation and surrender—a display of confidence by the patient in his own unconscious.

The individual is almost always in a face-to-face position with himself, with his own unconscious. It is uncommon for a patient to identify himself completely with his unconscious, with his instincts and feelings. Usually the personality is locked in combat with its own fundamentals. If one is to exert a definite influence on the patient, a necessary condition is to understand in detail this antagonism between the personality and its own unconscious. It is not those people whose unconscious is distinguished by the reliability, strength and steadiness of their feelings and instincts and who are aware that they are at one with their unconscious who come to the psychiatrist but those whose unconscious is confused, unreliable, erratic, those who are at war with their unconscious, with themselves and constantly sit, as it were, on a smouldering volcano.

(d) *Self-illumination* is a precondition for meaningful and effective attitudes towards oneself. The doctor wants to help the patient understand himself. We speak of analytical methods in this connection. They are rarely harmless, often they are disturbing, sometimes shattering. We may well ask ourselves who would risk stripping the individual psyche to its foundations, unless from the outset it is certain that the person will be able to stand by himself and live on his own resources once these have been freed, or that, should he seem powerless, some objective support will be ready to offer him help which he can accept.

Where general attitudes to life are concerned, everything depends on the personality of the psychiatrist and his own philosophical outlook. This raises so many difficulties and conflicts that the individual psychiatrist has to reach his decisions simply on the basis of instinctive conviction rather than by any process of scientific reasoning.

Having obtained an over-all view of psychotherapeutic methods, we can make some comparisons. In the first place, we will compare the different attempts made to promote recovery by a *modification of the life situation*.

The crudest, most superficial method is *a change in milieu*. The patient is removed from his accustomed environment and from the frictions and difficulties which have accumulated in his own personal world. He is then exposed to new stimuli and impressions. Observation is made whether this helps him and whether through the rest and reflection, through the change and the temporary liberation from the troubles of his personal world, he gains strength and can progress. The doctor brings about no inward change directly.

Occupation therapy submits psyche and body to ordinary life-requirements—instead of an empty passing of the time or being left entirely to oneself. It keeps the patient in touch with the world and is supposed to use what strength the patient has available for the restoration of his disordered functions through some form of activity.

Social work: The social worker, so far as this is practically possible, changes the life-situation by reducing hurtful stress. In addition, and also where such care is not possible, general advice in relation to the life-situation will help and so will positive attitudes on the part of everyone concerned.

In the second place, we will compare the different ways in which patients *experience the content* of their psychotherapeutic relationship with the doctor. Mere acknowledgment of what the doctor says, merely thinking about it and considering it, has no real effect. Contents, interpretations, view-points and goals all have to be a matter of actual experience before they can take proper effect. This may happen in a number of different ways:

Ideas are given picture-form and thus impress more vividly. Only so do they take effect in waking-suggestion or in hypnosis. The suggestor must see to it that what he says has a pictorial quality which will engage the imagination.

There has to be a desired goal. Something has to enter *the behaviour-tendency* that is compelling and unavoidable. This is induced by authoritative requests, compelling commands, sometimes issued bluntly in the form of abrupt orders or shouting at the patient.

Symbols in the form of archaic images, contents of universal appeal, have *to be substantially there and believed in.* There is a particular gratification which comes from a revelation of what actually is. This fortifies the patient's own awareness of being with something fundamental, which gives to his inner attitudes both resonance and shape. The therapist who works along such lines finds himself the prophet of a faith.

In counselling and instructing the patient how to look at his real situation, at his personal world and at himself, the important thing is that he should implement a decisive Yes and No. It is no help to him just to learn something; there has to follow a certain vision of things, and if they are to be mastered, *a recognition and taking over of them.* It is the individual's responsibility to decide what he will assimilate and what he will reject. His own existential decision ultimately determines his actual way of life. It is beyond any psychotherapist to make him achieve this. The most he can do in his communication with the patient is to develop possibilities in the conversational interchange which may afford unpredictable opportunities for an awakening.

In Macbeth the doctor utters a harsh truth. Macbeth asks him: How does your patient, doctor?

DOCTOR: Not so sick my Lord,
    As she is troubled with thick-coming fancies,
    That keep her from her rest.

MACBETH: Cure her of that;
    Canst thou not minister to a mind diseased;
    Pluck from the memory a rooted sorrow;
    Raze out the written troubles of the brain;
    And with some sweet oblivious antidote,
    Cleanse the stuff'd bosom of that perilous stuff
    Which weighs upon the heart?

DOCTOR: *Therein the patient*
    Must minister to himself.

II

THE MEANING OF MEDICAL PRACTICE
IN PSYCHOTHERAPY

THE RELATION OF KNOWLEDGE TO PRACTICE

IT is demanded of psychopathology that it should serve practice
and not infrequently it is blamed for not doing so. A sick person
should be helped, a doctor is there to heal. His function is all too
easily damaged by his preoccupation with pure science. Knowledge
on its own is useless and pure science results in therapeutic nihilism.
Once we know what is there, can recognize it and safely predict
what will be its course, the feeling grows that there is nothing more
to do but hand the patients over to some kind of care, without
expecting that we can really help them. This, so it has been suggested,
might be a particular danger in respect of the severe psychoses and
inborn abnormalities of personality.

On the other hand there exists an optimistic desire to be of help.
Something should be done or attempted in all circumstances.
People believe in effecting cure. Knowledge loses in interest when
it does not serve any therapeutic purpose. If science fails one, then
there is faith in one's art and good fortune; at any rate one will
contrive an atmosphere of cure, even if this is only some therapeutic
establishment that ticks over idly.

Both therapeutic nihilism and therapeutic over-enthusiasm are
equally irresponsible. In both cases critical judgment is lost, on
the one hand when passivity wrongly tries to justify to itself that
nothing can be done and on the other hand when blind activity
seems to think that goodwill and enthusiasm are in themselves
worth while and can achieve something: that is, practice only needs
aptitude not knowledge. But in the long run effective practice can
only be based on the certainties of knowledge.

Practice in its turn becomes a means to knowledge. It not only
achieves just what was intended but unexpected things as well. Thus
therapeutic schools unwittingly foster the phenomena which they

cure. In Charcot's time there was a wealth of hysterical phenomena which almost disappeared from the scene once interest in them had vanished. So too in the days when hypno-therapy emanated from Nancy and dominated the picture, hypnotic phenomena came into being all over Europe to an extent never witnessed again since then. Every school of psychotherapy, with its own defined outlook, technical and psychological points of view, has its own typical patients. In sanatoria, we find the products of sanatorium life. None of this is intended and as soon as we recognize the connection, we want to find a remedy.

The basic fact remains that, through contact with patients, psychotherapeutic intervention and the actual experience of effect and counter-effect open up possibilities of knowledge which can never be gained when the risks of therapeutic experiment are merely contemplated. 'We have to act to deepen our knowledge,' says v. Weizsäcker.

Therapeutic intentions and the experiences which can only be arrived at through therapeutic activity provide us with a system of psychopathology which gives practical orientation to our scientific knowledge and enables us to evaluate and order it from this practical point of view. Textbooks of psychotherapy are therefore to some extent the same as those of psychopathology. They are, it is true, limited by the practical horizon, but in so far as they report upon experience, they introduce something essential for the completeness of psychopathological theory.

The Contingent Nature of all Therapy

All therapy, psychotherapy and attitudes to patients depend upon the State, religion, social conditions, the dominant cultural tendencies of the age and finally, but never solely, on accepted scientific views.

The *State* lays down, or moulds by its policies, the basic human relationships, the organization of help and security, the utilization of resources, the giving or withholding of rights. There is no guardianship or detention in mental hospitals without State powers. Whatever the therapy, an arbitrary element is present which derives in the last resort from the authority and demands of the State. Every consultation takes place within a situation in which the doctor has effective authority, heightened by the clinic and his own official position. Where there is no statutory power to give a basis for this, power must necessarily be exercised through an authority, which in that case has to be personally acquired.

Religion, or its absence, determines the aim of the therapeutic relationship. When doctor and patient are bound by the same faith, they recognize something other than themselves that gives final decisions, judgment, direction and sets the frame within which the particular psychotherapeutic measures can take place. When these conditions are absent, the place of religion is taken by a secular philosophy. The doctor takes over the functions of the priest. There is as it were the idea of a worldly confession, consultations for the public on matters of the soul. Once the objective group sanction is put aside, psychotherapy becomes in danger of being more than just a means; it may become the expression of a more or less confused philosophy of life, an absolute one or one that changes like a chameleon, serious or mock-serious but always personal and private.

Sharing in something objective—whether symbols, a faith, the accepted philosophy of some group—is a necessary condition for any profound cohesion among men. People very rarely stick together as individuals out of a personal loyalty or simply find happiness in a transcendent destiny shared with one other human being. Many modern psychotherapists labour under the illusion that, when faced with neuroses and personality disorders, the highest possible expectation is: realization of the patient's own self, development of his powers of synthetic reasoning and a balanced human fulfilment in terms of his own personal pattern. Psychotherapy must be set within a frame of common beliefs and values. If not, the individual is thrown back to an extreme degree on his own resources, and even if he can respond only minimally to this, psychotherapy becomes nothing else than superfluous; if, however, in the total atmosphere of disbelief, the individual cannot respond at all, psychotherapy may only too easily become a smoke-screen for his failure.

Social conditions determine the innumerable situations in which the individual finds himself. The financial level of a social class, for example, may well determine the psychotherapeutic measures, which all cost time and therefore money when they demand long-term probing of the individual patient.

Science creates those pre-conditions for knowledge which are necessary for definite goals in therapy. But science itself does not provide the goal though it gives us means for reaching it. Science, when it is genuine, makes statements that are of general validity. At the same time it is critical, for it knows what it does *not* know. Practice is dependent on science only in its methods, not as regards its aims.

In actual practice there are temptations to evade this situation, that is, evade the dependence on science and the fact that science is insufficient to provide us with all the reasons for our actions. Things are expected from science which it can never provide. In this age of superstitious belief in science, science is used to conceal unanswerable facts. Where decision can only be a matter of personal responsibility, science is called on to give an answer, on the basis of its general validity, as if it knew, even when in fact no such knowledge exists. Science, thus, seems to provide reasons for what has in fact come about through quite other necessities. This is the case when the doctor misses the mark in certain cases of compensation neuroses, criminal responsibility and in many of his psychotherapeutic directives.

A form of pseudo-science may be used to express something that is by no means known but only wished for, something simply conceived of, wanted and believed in. Science is then made plastic to suit the purposes of practice. A therapy that pacifies, obscures and reassures gives rise to conceptual schemata that are turned to the purposes of a therapy that asserts, decides, permits and forbids. Science becomes a convention and lends a scientific tone to psychotherapeutic practice analogous to the theological climate of earlier times.

A line of demarcation, therefore, has to be drawn within all types of therapeutic practice. Everything that is sufficiently grounded in general scientific presuppositions (which must be *de facto* accepted as valid) has to be separated from everything that is based on a religion (or on a concept of the universe or on a philosophy), or the lack of such: it is from this that stems the whole direction, or lack of direction of the therapy, its whole style or lack of style, its specific atmosphere and colour.

LEGAL STEPS, EXPERT OPINION AND PSYCHOTHERAPY

Psychiatric patients may sometimes break the Law, become alarming or at any rate somewhat eerie to those around them. Something has to be done about them. The medical motive here is twofold. In the interests of society such patients have to be made *harmless*. In the interests of the patients, themselves, some attempt must be made at *cure*.

In many cases *public safety* demands the committal of the patient to hospital. He needs to be protected from doing violence. We want moreover to take him out of the public eye. We vary the form of segregation and try to make it humane so that relatives are satisfied and public conscience is appeased. Our own concept and interpretation of insanity involuntarily cause us to hide it away although it is one of the basic facts of human reality. In all our actions and thoughts we tend to simplify and dispose of it, free ourselves from looking at it properly, minimize its reality in our interpretation of it and make everything as comfortable as possible.

The interest of the patient calls for *therapy*. Committal to hospital is necessary for his own sake; for instance, to prevent suicide, to feed him, and carry out all possible therapeutic measures.

In actual practice there is a tacit presupposition that we all know what is sickness and what is health. Where this is a matter of common agreement and generally valid as with the majority of somatic illnesses, organic psychoses such as General Paralysis and the most severe forms of mental illness, there is no problem but there is a considerable one when we come to the vast number of milder cases, particularly the personality disorders (psychopathies) and the neuroses.

Whether the person is mentally ill or not is the practical measure for decisions in the individual case. How this decision is arrived at throughout different ages and situations has always been a matter for the Authorities in conjunction with the extent of insight of the time.

The question of whether a person is mentally ill or not gains special significance when there is a judgment to be made on the '*degree of free-will in offenders*'. Any clear-cut definition of an act of free-will is always of a practical nature. Science has no technical knowledge of freedom; it can only say something about empirical facts—whether a patient knows what he did and knows that it is forbidden, whether he acted wilfully and whether he is aware it was against the Law. Concerning free-will itself, science can only judge according to the given conventional ruling, which ascribes or denies psychic freedom in certain states that can be empirically ascertained. On the matter of freedom, Damerow (1853) wrote: 'Just a few of the patients in this mental institution (1,100) are or have been responsible for their actions all the time.' According to this the diagnosis of illness as such never precludes an act of free-will. This can only be determined by analysis of the individual's state at the time of the act. However, conventional procedure is apt to work out differently. For instance, a man in a normal state of alcoholic intoxication, however severe, is regarded as being in possession of free-will, but not if he is in some unusual state of intoxication. The diagnosis of General Paralysis as such precludes free-will. I will illustrate practical difficulties with two brief examples from my own experiences as a psychiatric expert in Court before the first World War:

A postman in the country, who had always carried out his duties properly, committed a small theft. It was found out that he had been in a mental hospital in the past. He was referred for an opinion. Consideration of the old case-history showed he undoubtedly had had a schizophrenic episode (schub). Because the old history was known, it was possible in the present examination to identify with confidence certain symptoms as schizophrenic. The diagnosis was clear. At that time schizophrenia (dementia praecox) was conventionally as valid a reason as General Paralysis for the abrogation of criminal responsibility. (The confusion of the concept of schizophrenia which arose later and which let it merge into normality was not then in use.) The man was quiet, composed and not obviously ill but he was, nevertheless, described by the expert on the grounds of the above diagnosis as an ill man who came under Section 51 of the Criminal Code. The Public Prosecutor was most indignant, everyone, including the expert, was a bit taken aback and thought it strange, but the Law operated automatically for his acquittal.

The second example was a typical case of pseudologia; the patient used to have periods when his fantastic abilities ran riot and he had once more committed a series of frauds. For three-quarters of an hour in the Court over which von Lilienthal the famous criminologist was presiding I described the romantic story of this life of crime. I also showed how the behaviour was limited to certain periods, how the offender seemed to be precipitated into it with headaches, etc., and drew the conclusion that one was dealing with an hysteric, a variation of personality not a disease process. One could not free him from criminal responsibility, at any rate at the beginning of the frauds, but the impression of some inner compulsion, made aesthetically convincing perhaps by my sensational description, led the Court to acquit the man contrary to expert opinion.

The field of psychotherapy has to be kept apart from all these legal measures and expert opinions. Psychotherapy is an attempt to use psychic communication in order to help the patient explore the inner depths of his mind and find there some hold whereby he may regain the road to health. Psychotherapy was formerly a haphazard procedure but in the last few decades it has become an extensive problem of practice. The fundamentals of it need to be clear before we can make any judgments about it, whether these will be of a negative sort or highly partisan in character.

THE LINK WITH DIFFERENT LEVELS OF GENERAL MEDICAL THERAPY

What the doctor does towards cure happens at various levels of meaning for the patient. A number of stages of therapeutic activity have to be conceived. Each stage has limits where it ceases to be effective and a leap up has to be made to the next level.

(a) The doctor removes a tumour surgically, opens an abscess, gives quinine against malaria, salvarsan against syphilis. In such instances he applies his *technical knowledge of cause and effect* and through mechanical and chemical means repairs the *disturbed connections in the apparatus of life*. This area of therapy is the most effective and best understood in its effects. Its *limit* is everything living.

(*b*) The doctor *submits the living being to certain conditions*, of diet, environment, rest or exertion, training, etc. Here he makes definite arrangements which will facilitate *the living being as a whole to help itself*. He behaves like a gardener in that he cultivates, fosters and according to results continually changes his procedure. This is the area of therapy in which it shows itself to be a rational art, based on an instinctive feeling for everything that lives. Its *limit* is the fact that man not only harbours a living being but is himself a thinking psyche.

(*c*) Instead of the doctor putting the body technically in order so far as its various parts are concerned, and so far as the body as a whole is concerned tending and nursing it, he addresses himself directly to the patient as *another rational being*. Instead of treating him as an object, he enters into communication with him. The patient *is to know* what is happening to him so that he will co-operate with the doctor in dealing with the illness as something alien. Both for doctor and patient the illness has become something objective and the treated patient remains outside the game as himself, while along with the doctor he furthers the success of the various therapeutic measures. But the patient also *wants to know* what is happening to him. He considers it undignified not to know. The doctor accepts this demand for freedom and without reservation will tell him everything he knows and thinks, leaving it to the patient as to what he does with this knowledge and how he comes to terms with it. The *limit* here is the fact that man cannot be relied on to be a rational creature, but is a thinking psyche and his thinking profoundly influences the vital existence of his body.

Fear and expectation, opinion and observation all have an immense effect on the body. Man does not face his own body simply and freely. The doctor, therefore, affects the body indirectly through what he communicates. The extreme case where an individual exercises nothing but a beneficial vital effect on his own body, despite all that he is told about it or can possibly think about it, is very rare. As a result the doctor cannot just tell the patient all that he knows and thinks about him but can only communicate things to him in such a way that the defenceless patient derives no harm.

The doctor must also see that the patient does not use the information in any vitally disastrous way.

In the rare case of a patient who is allowed to know everything, he must have the strength to balance up any objective knowledge critically and not let it grow into something absolute. This means that, even when things seem inevitable, he must see them as containing an element of the problematical and possible. Everything empirical has this property and even where a benign outcome is predicted almost with certainty, he would still need to remember the possible risks. Having this knowledge, he must be able to plan for the future sensibly and accept the chances of decline. Should the patient be allowed to know the full truth, anxiety would not have to gain the mastery in the shape of fear. This situation is an exception, if indeed it happens at all, so that doctors are faced with a new function: instead of communicating the full truth to a patient, they must constantly think of him in the totality of his body-psyche unity.

(d) This treatment of a patient as a body-psyche unity leads to a continual *aporia*. As a human being the patient has the right to be told in full what is happening to him. But inasmuch as he is a human being, he comes to grief because of his anxiety, which upsets what he knows with disastrous effects. The patient therefore loses his right to know. Theoretically, however, this painful position is not a final one, because the individual may mature in the direction of the exceptional case, where the full truth can be known and accepted. It is just in this intermediary position where the patient swings between feeling hopelessly imprisoned and affirming himself as a human being that *psychotherapy is supposed to help*.

Psychotherapy can take place while doctor and patient are both unaware. The doctor limits what he tells and speaks authoritatively; the patient duly accepts what he is told and does not think about it but has blind confidence in its certainty. Authority and submission remove anxiety in the doctor as well as in the patient. Both go on living in a pseudo-certainty. In view of the relativity of all medical knowledge, the doctor, in so far as he is aware of this, may become uncertain himself and to that extent his authority will suffer, which protects his own feeling of uncertainty like a mask. If however the doctor, in his superior position, surrenders his authority by imparting some criticism of his inevitably limited knowledge, the patient's anxiety will grow and as a result of this unreserved honesty the doctor will find it impossible to be a doctor in this particular situation. For this reason doctor and patient instinctively adhere to authority as something reassuring. The sensitiveness of the doctor lest he should not be wholly believed and followed, and that of the patient, lest the doctor should not assert himself with complete certainty, mutually condition each other.

The unconscious state where psychotherapy occurs through exercise of authority becomes a conscious state when the doctor addresses his treatment to the patient as a body-psyche unity and for the first time begins to develop his psychotherapy in all kinds of directions. Now in contrast to unreserved communication from one person's reason to another's, the doctor will break off communication unnoticed by the patient and on his behalf since it is the doctor who now controls the limits. The doctor draws inwardly to a distance (though he does not show it), takes the whole individual as his object and weighs up the effects of his entire therapy within which every word will be controlled. The patient is no longer freely told what the doctor may think or feel but each word, each act of the doctor has to be in principle calculated as to its psychic effect. From the doctor's point of view, patient and doctor have distanced themselves completely, while the patient on his side thinks he feels a personal closeness. The doctor turns himself into a function of the therapeutic process.

This mode of acting can range over an extraordinarily wide field, from quite crude measures to far-reaching, philosophical designs. The so-called '*Ueberrumpelungstherapie*' (bowling the patient over), electrical hocus-pocus, imposed changes of environment, hypnosis, authoritative requests and commands, are all recipes of a drastic therapeutic attack and frequently successful in relation to certain symptoms. But procedures such as these have only limited application in practice and are hardly capable of further development or elaboration in depth. In the psychotherapeutic methods of depth-psychology—psychoanalysis and psychosynthesis—and all its variants, higher level procedures are used which, nevertheless, always contain an element that depends on someone's belief in the truth of a theory.

The *limit* of all these psychotherapies is, *firstly*, the factual impossibility of any doctor achieving full distance (subjectivity in the form of sympathy or antipathy always intervenes); and the further impossibility of his ever being in possession of enough vitality and native psychic vigour to influence the patient's psyche, on his own. Somehow he has to share himself in the beliefs which the patient is expected to accept. *Secondly*, there is the basic impossibility of objectifying any individual fully, thus making him an object for treatment. Once a person is fully objectified, he is never his real self. But what he himself is and what he becomes is in the last resort an essential for the development or cure of his neurotic symptoms. In relation to the individual himself and his potential true Existence, the doctor can only act within the concrete, historical situation, where the patient is no longer just a case but a human destiny that unfolds in the light of its own self-illumination. Once the individual has turned into an object, he can be treated by technical means, nursing care and skill, but the individual as himself can only discover himself through the mutual sharing of destinies.

(*e*) Therefore what is left as the ultimate thing in the doctor-patient relationship is *existential communication*, which goes far beyond any therapy, that is, beyond anything that can be planned or methodically staged. The whole treatment is thus absorbed and defined within a community of two selves who live out the possibilities of Existence itself, as reasonable beings. For example, there are no rules deriving from some supposed assessment of the individual as a whole which determine whether the person shall conceal or reveal; nor is the whole thing quite fortuitous, as if the person could listen to everything and then be left to his own devices. One questions and gropes from one freedom to another within the concreteness of the actual situation, taking no responsibility for the other nor making any abstract demands. Concealment has to be decried as much as revelation should this happen as a mere intellectual performance without any mutual sharing of destinies. Doctor and patient are both human beings and as such are fellow-travellers in destiny. The doctor is not a pure technician nor pure authority, but Existence itself for its own sake, a transient human creature like his patient. There is no final solution.

The *limit* is the fact that individuals can only share their destiny as fellow-travellers within the frame of what is called transcendent being. Mere subjective existence does not bind persons together, nor does Existence itself as such. For in individuals Existence itself, although entirely free when in the world, is still by its very nature something given only by Transcendence, from which it knows itself derived.

If one recalls now the various meanings of medical therapy, having followed all the stages we have considered above to the point where therapy comes to an end and its place is taken by the full human interchange, which guides but can never itself conduct any therapy, then the psychiatrist's (Psychotherapist's) knowledge and activity will be seen to acquire a *specific meaning of their own within the art and practice of medicine*. By virtue of his speciality, the psychiatrist alone considers the individual consciously and method- ically as a whole, not as one of his organs nor yet as an entire body with no reference to anything else. The psychiatrist alone is accus- tomed to take the social situation into account, the environment, the personal history and the experiences of the patient, and con- sciously give them a place in his therapeutic plan. Doctors are equipped for this comprehensive task, in so far as they are psychia- trists.

The final, decisive occurrence in any patient's therapy can be called 'revelation'. The patient becomes clear to himself, first by taking in the doctor's communicated knowledge and learning certain details about himself; secondly, by seeing himself as it were in a mirror, and learning something of what he is like; thirdly, by bringing himself out further through an inner activity in which he gets to know himself more deeply; and fourthly, by establishing and filling out the revelation of himself in the course of existential communication. This process of clarification is an essential feature of psychotherapy but it must not be simplified because it is a structured whole and we shall only be led astray if one stage is taken for the other. This process of clarification in the shape of the self- revelation of an individual extends far beyond what may be acces- sible to any psychotherapeutic plan. It carries one on into the philosophical realm of the individual growth of a self.

If we take the extremes, there is a radical difference in the meaning of therapy according to whether the doctor addresses himself to the patient's primary self, tries to clarify this at all levels and makes effective communication by acting as a partner in revelation, or whether he directs his therapeutic efforts at pathological mechanisms only, uses the methods of the natural sciences and tries to influence the situation by physical and psychological means. Better self-understanding may be followed by recovery of the pathological mechanisms because in this case they only became affected when the patient's inner psychic life falsified his existential possibilities. But pathological mechanisms can also come about without any such context. They may even arise within the context of some genuine upsurge of Existence itself. In that case they need a fundamentally different approach than that offered by depth-psychology and psychotherapy.

Thus in therapy the widest polarities lie in whether the doctor turns to what can be discovered by science, that is, to the biological event, or whether he turns to the freedom of man. A mistake is made about the whole of human life, should the doctor in looking at persons let them be submerged in the biological event; so too should he convert human freedom into that sort of being which, like nature, is empirically there and can be used technically as an instrument of therapy. Life I can treat, but to freedom, I can only appeal.

Types of Inner Obstacle—the Patient's Decision to undergo Psychotherapy

There are three types of inner obstacle; first, there is the absolute obstacle that human nature cannot be changed in its essence, but only modified superficially; secondly, there is the obstacle of an individual's inner psychological 'set'; and thirdly, there is the primary obstacle of the self. The first type of obstacle can be tackled in a way analogous to the training of animals, the second by re-education and discipline, the third can become the target for existential communication. Every person will come upon these obstacles in himself. He may train himself, educate himself and communicate with himself towards better self-illumination. But should he enter into relationship with another person over this, then in the first instance (training) he becomes purely an object. In the second instance (re-education) he keeps relatively good touch with the other but yet there is a distance kept, which gives scope for attitudes of deliberate instruction. In the third instance, he is himself linked with the other's destiny and confronts him on the same level with a perfect openness of approach.[1] Training is nothing but a soulless manœuvre; re-education uses mental content, with discussion always taking place under authoritative conditions; existential communication is a mutual self-illumination, which remains essentially an event in time and does not signify any generally applicable insight into the individual case. Real it may be, but it cannot become a therapeutic instrument for use in any planned, deliberate way.

In spite of people's need for help, they are not only disinclined towards psychotherapy but to any kind of medical treatment. There is something in them that prefers self-help. This inner obstacle is an obstacle which they want to overcome by themselves. Hence Nietzsche's remark: 'Should anyone give advice to a patient, he acquires a feeling of superiority over him, whether the advice is accepted or not. For this reason, irritable and proud patients hate their advisers even more than their illness.'

The situation gets easier only if patient and doctor work together against the illness as if it were something alien to them both. Thus patient and doctor face the disturbance together with an equal self-detachment. But if the psyche has to declare itself in need of treatment, it resists on principle. The person feels himself as quite different psychically from what he feels about himself bodily. The obstacle which the self sets up permits the individual indeed to form loving and fighting relationships with some other self but not to accept a dependence and guidance which will determine his innermost life without his being aware of it. (This is not the accepted guidance as to what one is to do and how one is to act in the external world.) There are two preconditions then for psychotherapy. One is the person's awareness of ordinary human weakness, which accepts the notion that some sort of inner guidance is necessary and so he is ready to put himself in the hands of a personal counsellor; he does not lower his stock in any way by these

[1] Regarding modes of communication—see my *Philosophie*, Bd. II, the chapter on communication.

views, since he simply permits himself what every man needs. The other precondition is that he has a specific awareness of illness. The decision that 'I am mentally sick' determines the decision for psychiatric treatment since therapy is needed only by somebody who is ill.

However, we know that the concept of illness has many ambiguities. The statement that one is ill can mean, for instance: one cannot master one's own psychic happenings, or there is some reduction in performance, there is suffering or a failure to accept responsibility for one's own inadequacy, one's drives and feelings or for one's own actions.

The decision to accept oneself as ill means something like a *capitis diminutio*—a lowering of the flag. The psychic phenomena in question are not like a cold or a pneumonia, nor like general paralysis or a brain-tumour, dementia praecox or epilepsy. They are still phenomena within the realm of freedom. A need for therapy here signifies acceptance of loss of freedom, though in fact freedom is still there and maintains its rights at the same time as it renounces them. If, however, a series of psychic phenomena end in loss of responsibility because free-will has become enslaved, any possibility of trusting the individual, giving him some responsible function or gaining reasonable co-operation is inevitably limited from the start. As a result everyone who is independent, realistic or has any sort of faith at all recoils from psychotherapeutic ways which penetrate the psychic depths and concern themselves with the person as a whole. But where the individual as a whole is not concerned and there is some possibility for more specific techniques in psychotherapy, hypnosis for instance, autogenic training or physical exercises, etc., there is no question of dealing with the human psyche as such; we simply use psychic techniques for a limited purpose (e.g. for ridding a patient of certain physical complaints). Even then, because they are *psychic* techniques, the question still remains whether personal embarrassment or self-esteem will permit their use.

In any case we cannot deny that the decision to undergo psychotherapy is a decision indeed and means something like an irrevocable choice in anyone's life, for better or for worse.

THE AIMS AND LIMITS OF PSYCHOTHERAPY

What does the patient want to achieve when he goes to a psychiatrist? What does the doctor see as his treatment-goal? 'Health' in some undefined sense. But for one person 'health' means an unthinking, optimistic, steady equilibrium through life, for another it means an awareness of God's constant presence and a feeling of peace and confidence, trust in the world and the future; while a third person believes himself healthy when all the unhappiness of his life, the activities which he dislikes, all that is wrong in his situation is covered up by deceptive ideals and fictitious explanations. And perhaps there is no small number of those whose health and happiness is best enhanced by the treatment Dr. Relling proffered in Ibsen's *The Wild Duck*: 'I take care', he says, 'to preserve his life-lie', and talking about the 'fever for justification' he remarks sarcastically, 'If you take away the average person's life-lie, you rob him of his happiness too.' However much truthfulness is desirable in therapy—a view we support unreservedly—it is all the same prejudicial to imagine that untruth makes people ill. There are people whose vitality thrives on untruthfulness both towards themselves and the world at large. We must, therefore, consider all the more carefully *what cure means* and what are the limits of psychotherapeutic effort although there are no final answers to these questions.

(1) *The question—what is cure?* With every kind of therapy there is a tacit understanding that everyone knows what cure means. There is usually no problem so far as somatic illnesses are concerned but in the case of the neuroses and personality disorders (psychopathies), the situation is different. Cure becomes linked inseparably with what we call faith, general philosophical outlook or personal morality although the relationship is a highly ambiguous one (containing both truth and falsehood). It is pure fiction to believe that the doctor only confines himself to what has been thought healthy and objectively desirable by philosophy and religion.

J. H. Schultz, for example, discusses the aim of therapy in relation to the 'autogenous states of relaxation' which he investigated.

They are said to be 'independent of any philosophical attitude' since in psychotherapy 'the individual is the measure of all things'; autogenous states 'serve that unique self-realization which is proper for life'. The highest aim of psychotherapy is said to be 'the self-realization of the patient', the 'developing and shaping of the full human status, that of harmonious freedom'. 'Autogenous relaxation', he says, 'by means of this self-directed introspection simply extends a work which it is most appropriate for personality to perform upon itself.' These are rather vague and dubious formulations. States of relaxation have been used for thousands of years in the techniques of Yoga, in all methods of mystical contemplation, in the exercises of the Jesuits—but always with a difference. The aim in these states has always been the existential meaning of the experiences, the attainment of something absolute and unconditioned; the goal has never been the exercise of a psychic technique nor the individual's own empirical state, presupposed as immanently perfectible by him. Schultz has dropped these tenets of faith and retains only the technique (which as a result he was the first to investigate empirically and methodically). He lost sight therefore of the deeper effects of these states on the individual's awareness of being, ignores the metaphysical sources of experience and misses the existential vigour and sharp seriousness of all these activities. He confines himself to empirical medical effects but unwittingly he uses formulations of the treatment-goal which substitute for the earlier impulses of faith and already presuppose a certain philosophical outlook on his part —roughly that of a bourgeois individualism that has deviated rather from the level of Goethean humanism, and from which I am sure Schultz himself is far removed. Formulations such as these presuppose a final definition of man, though in fact what this is remains highly obscure.

The statement of v. Weizsäcker may be quoted in contrast. He says: 'It is the ultimate destiny of man, precisely, that can never be made the object of any therapy; it would be blasphemous.' He clearly expresses the indefiniteness of any therapeutic goal when he says: 'We can do much, if we are successful, in setting certain limits to morbid events and confining them in definite channels.' v. Weizsäcker knows that the therapeutic goal cannot be defined in scientific or human terms alone, but by something else in the world, that is extremely tangible: 'If we want to confine ourselves purely to human attitudes, these are limited by the social order.'

The aim of all psychotherapeutic effort is often quoted as 'health', capacity for work, ability to perform and enjoy (Freud), adaptation to society (Adler), delight in creation, a capacity for happiness. The uncertainty and multiplicity of such formulations indicate their doubtfulness.

We cannot rid ourselves entirely of some basic philosophical viewpoint when formulating our psychotherapeutic goals. This may get obscured or undergo chaotic changes but we cannot develop any psychotherapy that is purely medical, self-contained and appears to be its own justification. This holds even when isolated phenomena are under consideration. For instance, *to dispel anxiety* is generally thought to be a self-evident *therapeutic aim*. Gebsattel's dictum however is true: 'We are as doubtful whether we really want a life without anxiety as we are certain that we want a life without fear.' Large numbers, particularly of modern people, seem to live fearlessly because they lack imagination. There is as it were an impoverishment of the heart. This freedom from anxiety is but the other side of a deeper loss of freedom. Arousal of anxiety and with it of a more vital humanity might be just the task for someone possessed by Eros paidagogos (informing passion).

Prinzhorn formulates the exactly opposite goal when he first accepts the different psychotherapeutic schools as something unavoidably sectarian in character (though on another occasion he sees psychotherapy merging in future into the unity of medical practice). He explicitly argues that it is impossible for any psychotherapy to be autonomous from philosophy. He makes the psychotherapeutic task an exalted one, he sees the therapist 'mediating between an anxious loneliness and some living whole, some possibility of new community, the world itself and perhaps God'—but the therapist can only mediate through his unique *personality*, through a mental suppleness that lacks objectivity, lacks any sanction for what is done or said; or else because he is a member of some intimate, cultural community, religious, national or party-political; only thus is he able to return firm answers when questions of authority arise. '*The purely personal element* in therapy *can only be removed* by making some reference to a higher power in the name of which the therapist acts. In that case the sectarian character of the psycho-therapeutic schools is no deviancy, but rather the direct consequence of a necessary development.'

(2) *The limits of psychotherapy. The possibility of what is to be achieved* must determine the treatment-goal. There are certain insurmountable limits to psychotherapy and there are these two in particular:

(*a*) Therapy cannot be a *substitute for something that only life itself can bring.* For instance, we can only become transparently ourselves through a lifetime of loving communication in the course of a destiny shared with others. On the other hand such clarification as is brought about by psychotherapeutic means always remains something limited, objective, theoretical and restricted by authority. A professional performance constantly repeated on behalf of many never reaches the goal which only engagement in mutuality can attain. Further, life brings responsible tasks, perforce, and there are the real demands of work which no therapy however artful can contrive.

(*b*) A person is *originally thus and no other* and therapy finds itself confronted with this factor which it cannot alter. I in my freedom may confront this fact that I am thus and no other, con-front it as something I may change or at least transform through acceptance, but any therapy of others has to reckon with unalter-able elements, the mark of some lasting essence, something inborn. It is true we cannot say what this is in any given case but it is a basic experience of every doctor that where this 'being thus and no other' is the cause of the patient's distress, it provides an in-surmountable obstacle which will frustrate every therapeutic attempt. In the face of this 'being thus and no other', therapy finds itself at a loss. The therapeutic attitude can only retain its integrity if it accepts that fundamentally. When vexed by the question of which among all the given facts he must accept and which he can hope to modify, every thoughtful psychopathologist feels the constant impulse to clarify this unchangeable element, try to re-identify it and lift it to the level of a diagnostic quantity. But he has a wide field to play over. Either the unchangeable element is obscured since therapy aims at reassuring and deceiving, measures are adopted '*ut aliquid fiat*' and the aim becomes not so much the cure of an illness as the creation of an atmosphere of friendly help; one supports the 'life-lie' and avoids 'encroaching' too far. Or on the other hand there is open action, the therapist tries to get the individual himself to achieve adequate self-understanding; he does not undertake to relieve him but endeavours to give him some clarification. This means some way of life has to be found even for those with personality disorders (psychopaths) and every kind of personality. Wherever the person's nature is really abnormal, Nietzsche's saying may seem true: 'Every nature has its own philosophy, so has everyone who is unhappy, evil or exceptional.' In psychotherapy we have to resign ourselves in the end to patience, to a 'psychiatric tolerance', even towards the oddest and most irritating of people.

Therapeutic effort is limited both by the reality of the environment and by the patient being 'thus and no other'. Because of this, therapy in the end always becomes some kind of philosophical undertaking. Should it choose to illumine rather than obscure, it will have to teach humility and renunciation as well as the need to grasp at positive possibilities. Obviously this is not something that psychology or medicine can accomplish but only the close collaboration of doctor and patient in a mutual philosophic faith.

THE PERSONAL ROLE OF THE DOCTOR

We have seen that in the *doctor-patient relationship, authority* is always present and may have beneficial effects. In the rare case should true communication be achieved, it is lost again immediately, unless authority is entirely discarded. Usually, however, authority is needed and the doctor must never use his physical, social and psychological superiority as if it were absolute and the patient no longer a human being like the doctor. Attitudes of authority, like scientific attitudes, are only a part, never the whole, of the doctor's attitude to the patient.

In psychotherapy the demand for the personal involvement of the doctor is so heavy that complete gratification only occurs in isolated cases, if at all. v. Weizsäcker formulated the demand as follows: 'Only when the doctor has been deeply touched by the illness, infected by it, excited, frightened, shaken, only when it has been transferred to him, continues in him and is referred to himself by his own consciousness—only then and to that extent can he deal with it successfully.'

Communication, however, is usually distorted by the patients' typical needs. One of the relationships between individuals which is of importance for the psychiatrist is that which Freud describes as a '*transference*' of admiring, loving and also hostile feelings on to the doctor. This transference is unavoidable in psychotherapy and it can be a dangerous reef on which to break if we do not recognize it and deal with it. Many doctors bask in the superior position that has been foisted on them by their patients. On the other hand, the desire of many other doctors to dismiss all these transferences, submissions and dependencies, these one-sided erotic relationships in order to create the one desired relationship of understanding communication founders on the elementary needs of the patients who simply want someone they can dearly love and who will save them.

Responsible psychiatrists will turn *their own psychology*, the psychology of the doctor, into *an object for their conscious reflection*. Indeed the relationship between doctor and patient is far from unambiguous. Expert information, friendly help on equal terms, the authority of a doctor's order, all have essentially different meanings. Often there is a struggle between doctor and patient, sometimes a struggle for superiority, sometimes for clarification. Deep illumination comes either on the basis of an absolute authority in which someone believes, or on the basis of a mutual relationship, which implies that the doctor has to study himself as well as the patient.

We have no objective picture of what the contemporary psychotherapist in fact is like. *He has to be a philosopher*, consciously or no, methodically or haphazardly, in earnest or not, spontaneously or following contemporary fashions. It is not theory but his example which teaches us what manner of man he may be. The art of therapy, of relationship, gesture and attitude cannot be reduced to a few simple rules. We can never anticipate how reason and compassion, presence of mind and frankness, will show themselves in the given moment nor what will be their effect. The greatest possibility of all has been expressed in the Hippocratic sentence: *iatros philosophos isotheos*.

DIFFERENT PSYCHIATRIC ATTITUDES

Successful psychiatrists necessarily correspond in their natures to the needs and desires of 'nervous patients', since the mass of patients decide who is to be the successful therapist, and not the actual value or correctness of the doctor's own views or behaviour. Obviously, therefore, the greatest successes of all have not belonged to psychiatrists but to the shamans, priests, leaders of sects, wonder-workers, confessors and spiritual guides of earlier times.

The '*exercitia spiritualia*' of Ignatius Loyola were enormously successful and provide us with examples of real psychic cure; they were aimed at the control, arbitrary production and repression of every kind of emotion, affect or thought. Yoga techniques and the meditative exercises of Buddhism are also extraordinarily effective. In our own times perhaps the movement in the States for the cure of 'emotional disorders' or the cures at Lourdes have all had greater success (if we take mere numbers) than all the psychiatrists together. A few people may be helped to health by a stoic philosophy. Others again, even fewer, may be helped by Nietzsche's reckless honesty over the self.

All these movements can point to failures as well as successes. The '*exercitia spiritualia*' have been reported as bringing on 'religious mania'; and unstable people have been thrown off their balance by the doctrines of Nietzsche. If Freudian psychoanalysis produces its quota of conspicuous failures, symptomatic deterioration and painful suffering, this is common to all psychological methods when there is wholesale application of them. One type of patient will find one method suitable, another type will find another. Any therapy which wins success will be highly characteristic of the people of that time; it will have the contemporary features of its patients.

Our own age is characterized by the fact that psychiatrists are now performing in secular fashion what earlier was performed on the grounds of faith. The basic medical knowledge of the doctor derives from the natural sciences and constantly colours the situation but, whether he wants to or not, he is always exercising some psychological and moral influence. Since we have forced doctors into the role of performing an increasing number of functions that

formerly belonged to priests and philosophers, we now find ourselves with a great many different kinds of doctors. Once the
unity of faith is lacking, the needs of patients and doctors admit a
host of possibilities. How a psychiatrist acts will depend not only
on his general philosophical outlook and on his instinctive goals,
but also on the hidden pressure which the nature of his patients
exercises upon him. Obviously, therefore, *psychiatrists practise
many different types of psychotherapy.*

There is one group we can disregard; these are the credulous
stupids, who use untested methods and cure everyone by faradial
treatment, hypnotic or water treatments, powders and pills, and
who achieve successes by sheer force of personality, wherever
crude suggestion will do the trick. We also have the fraud, dishonest
with himself as with his patients; he uses the psychotherapeutic
relationship to assuage every possible kind of need both in himself
and his patients (sense of power, erotic drives, sensationalism).
The writings of these gentlemen have a characteristic tone and style;
they weave fantastic theories, show a contempt for other opinions,
a superiority derived from their naïve, confident assertions that
they alone are in sole possession of truth; they incline towards the
pathetic and the grandiose, tend to repeat simple propositions and
present us with *obiter dicta* which are supposed to deal with every
contradiction.

Then we find *the good doctor, the ingenuous individual* who
consciously confines himself to everything somatic and yet just
because of this unwittingly exercises a psychological effect, all the
more so as such an intention never enters his thoughts. Then there
are *the sceptics,* who possess an all-round scientific education and
see reality undisguised, yet still doubt what they know. They may
well give counsel to their patients and instruct them but they never
penetrate with any deep effect.

Were I to try and characterize *a type* of psychiatrist who *in this
scientific age* manages to remain balanced between the paradoxes
of all his various functions, yet touches all the psychic dimensions
with undoubted success, the following picture seems to take shape:
He is a man who has a solid background of somatic medicine,
physiology and the natural sciences. His attitude with his patients
is predominantly one of empirical observation, of factual assess-

ment and generally one that understands and appreciates reality. He will not easily find himself deceived nor will he readily adhere to any dogmas, fanaticisms or absolutisms. On the other hand he is without any fundamental convictions of his own and he has no knowledge of ultimates so he treats all dicta, facts, methods and terminologies as if they all belonged to the same general level of the sciences. His thinking does not form part of any comprehensive, conceptual system; this seems to him an advantage and he excuses the haphazard nature of his ideas by his own empirical attitude or by their supposedly heuristic value. The authority of science replaces the loss of all other authorities. He lives in a general atmosphere of conciliation and *laissez-faire* only broken on rare occasions when he uses moral indignation especially against the forces that threaten his profession. For him there is no such thing as absolute seriousness. He enjoys the laxity of a general basic scepticism, where the essential thing is to make the effective gesture and even his scientific attitude becomes such a gesture. His scientific ideas are tested and selected according to what success they acquire in the environment and with his patients. He genuinely play-acts, as it were, and adapts himself unconsciously to the situation. He does not rely on any serious, philosophic position but lets the following views support him: such and such a theory is true after its own fashion, but that other theory is also useful and none the less true. Profound scepticism enables him to leave the unhappy and needy patient some room for gratifying dreams and beliefs as the case and situation demand. Falsity is believed to be unavoidable but has to be kept under control and used for a purpose. This is the source for the solemn attitudes we meet, the sceptical smile, the ironical dignity, the engaging charm and the readiness to listen to anything unusual. Such doctors are phenomena of our present transition from the past ages of faith and learning to an era of positivistic materialism. Traditionally doctors are at home in the former and live on it as on a vanishing capital, but they also know their way about the latter so they are not to be pinned down to any one particular principle. We may pin them down to the principles of our times—that is, success, utility, scientific attitude, search for techniques and effective gestures—and we may believe that we see them, no longer as they are, but simply as their professional selves,

deeply interested in their work yet disengaged; the situation, however, forces us to pause. It is almost as if, 'in the very middle of
time' as one age goes down before the next, some spark of timeless
knowledge lights up within them.

If we are looking for the prototype of the *ideal psychiatrist*, the one
who will combine scientific attitudes of the sceptic with a powerful
impressive personality and a profound existential faith, Nietzsche's
words are not altogether inapt: 'No profession can be developed
to such great heights as that of the physician, especially since the
"spiritual doctors", the so-called "custodians of the soul" are no
longer permitted to practice magic arts and most educated people
tend to avoid them. No physician is thought to have reached the
highest level if he is simply well acquainted with the best and
most recent methods, versed in them and able to draw those
brilliant conclusions as to cause and effect that lead to diagnostic
fame. He must also be persuasive, adapt himself to each individual
and be able to bring innermost matters to light in his clients. He
needs to have a strong humanity which by its very appearance can
disperse timidity which is the force that undermines in any kind
of suffering. He should have the address of a diplomat, whether he
helps those to happiness who need it for their recovery or those who
need to give happiness for their health's sake (and can do so). He
needs the subtlety of a detective or a lawyer if he is to understand
people's secret souls without betraying that he does so—in short
nowadays the good physician requires the skill and vantage ground
of every other profession. Where he is so equipped, he can become
a benefactor to the whole of his society.'

There are no scientific grounds for determining what kind of
psychotherapist one will become nor the type which will be considered ideal. Certainly a psychotherapist should have a training
in somatic medicine and in psychopathology, both of which have
to be scientifically based. If he has no such training, he would only
be a charlatan, yet with this training alone he is still not a pyschotherapist. Science is only a part of his necessary equipment. Much
more has to be added. Among the *personal prerequisites*, the width
of his own horizon plays a part, so does the ability to be detached
at times from any value-judgment, to be accepting and totally
free of prejudice (an ability only found in those who generally

possess very well-defined values and have a personality that is mature). Finally, there is the necessity for fundamental warmth and a natural kindness. It is therefore clear that a good psychotherapist can only be a rare phenomenon and even then he is usually only good *for a certain circle of people* for whom he is well suited. A psychotherapist for everyone is an impossibility. However, force of circumstance makes it the psychotherapist's usual duty to treat everyone who may ask his help. That fact should help him to keep his claims to modest proportions.

HARMFUL PSYCHOLOGICAL ATMOSPHERES

People who have a faith or a philosophy will gain unintentional self-illumination in conjunction with their actual performance, they are led on by everything that befalls them, by ideas, by truth itself and by God. Self-reflection may serve them on the way but in itself it is never a primary force, it only becomes effective through actual being, which in turn lays hold of its help. But once self-reflection in the form of psychological study of the self becomes the whole atmosphere in which a person lives, there is no end to it since the person's psychic life is not yet Being itself but only a place where Being is envisaged. There is a dangerous tendency in psychotherapy to convert the psychic actuality of an individual into an end in itself. The person who turns his psyche into a god because he has lost both world and god finds himself standing finally in the void.

He misses the gripping force of things themselves, of objects of faith, images and symbols, tasks to perform, of anything absolute in the world. Psychological self-reflection can never achieve that which only becomes possible through a surrender to being. Here lie the radical differences between the purposeful manipulations of psychotherapists directed upon the psyche and the practices of priests, mystics and philosophers of all times, directed through the ages towards God or Being; between confidences, self-revelations given to the doctor and confession in church. The transcendent reality marks the difference. Mere psychological knowledge of possibilities and the use of psychological influences to bring the desired end about can never realize the possibilities in me. The individual must set about things, not about himself (or only about himself as a means); he must set about God not about faith, about Being not about Thinking, about something he loves not love itself, about performance not experience, about realization not about mere possibility—or rather he must set about all these alternatives as means of transit, not for their own sakes alone.

Within the psychological atmosphere an *egocentric attitude to life* develops, especially when the very opposite is intended, the individual as the subject of all this becomes the measure of all things. Existence thus becomes wholly relative as a result of this psychological knowledge which tends to absolutes and is taken as if it were the knowledge of what happens in fact.

A *specific brazenness* is fostered, a tendency to display one's psychic entrails, to say just that which is destroyed in the saying; there develops a curiosity over experience, an imposition on others of a purely psychological reality.

The murkiness which is always latent in this psychological atmosphere grows tangible when contrasted with the clear-cut activities of the general physician who does a clear and effective therapy in his own field, though he ignores the psychic elements and certainly misses a good deal by this, or when contrasted with the honesty of strong faith. Here the individual will do what he can within the framework of what is knowable, he puts up with everything else and leaves it to God without alleging any pseudo-psychological knowledge of it and without doing it violence or robbing it of its dignity.

However, we only need to know these psychological risks in order to meet them. So far as the objects and aims of psychology and psychotherapy are concerned, these are never an end in themselves but, once a high level of awareness has been reached, are instruments we cannot do without.

THE PUBLIC ASPECT OF PSYCHOTHERAPY

In the course of the last century and a half, the confinement of *mental patients* in institutions created a number of small worlds. Psychiatrists worked out the idea of reducing this problem to a minimum for both patients and society. *Diseases of the nervous system* were made a matter for independent clinics and for neuro-psychiatrists, but the neuroses and endogenous psychoses are no more closely related to the known neurological illnesses than they are to the other somatic disorders. *Psychotherapy* became a somewhat haphazard performance carried out by psychiatrists, neurologists and general physicians, without any basis of orderly principle. It is only during the last few decades that psychotherapy has become a profession on its own, and the status of psychotherapist became established. Psychotherapists were mostly doctors but they were supplemented by psychotherapists who were psychologists with a different training. Psychotherapy became the subject-matter of special journals. Congresses of psychotherapists came to number more than 500 participants. In 1936 something happened that was fundamentally new. The 'Deutsche Institut für Psychologische Forschung und Psychotherapie' was founded in Berlin under M. H. Göring. This was the last step whereby psychotherapy became institutionalized.

In this public sense psychotherapy has to establish itself as a branch of medical therapeutics in its own right. The exercise of the profession, therefore, has to be put under conditions which will serve the best performance. There has to be a possibility for training and instruction and the necessary psychological knowledge needs to be linked methodically with practice. This means that a number of scattered efforts have to be co-ordinated. Everything that has been initiated by individual endeavour and developed within cliques and schools must now shape itself into some integrated whole. The Institute tries to establish an interchange of mutual influence between all the forces of psychological knowledge and skill. The intention is to bridge the opposites, establish what all forms of psychotherapy have in common and demonstrate the unity of the idea. An out-patient department serves a practice which increases steadily. It is hoped to gain an extensive basis for research by regularly working through the case-histories. In this way, perhaps for the first time, it would prove possible to amass a number of psychotherapeutic biographies.

The main deficiency of this initial institution is that it functions apart from any psychiatric clinic. Psychotherapists who have no sound knowledge of the psychoses gained from their own experience and no contact with them in institutional practice can easily make fatal mistakes of diagnosis; they also fall victims to the fantastic nonsense which occupies so much space in the psychotherapeutic literature. When there is no proper grounding in the reality of the psychoses and no passionately sought understanding of them, every individual or anthropological presentation will, from the reality point of view, carry serious flaws. If we are to study man properly we have to take into account both the openness of unrestricted possibility and the limitations imposed by the real impenetrability of what is not understandable. These limitations only receive confirmation through the practice of psychiatry, the openness will only come to us through philosophy. Psychotherapy cannot live simply on its own resources.

Psychotherapy, as we have seen, has its roots in medicine but in its *contemporary reality* it has gone far beyond the field of medicine. As a phenomenon it belongs to an age poor in faith in the sense of an ecclesiastical tradition. Psychotherapy nowadays not only wants to help the neurotic but mankind itself in all its spiritual and personal needs. It is significantly, though not traditionally, linked with confession, unburdening of the soul, the care of souls as in the ages of faith. Psychotherapy makes demands and gives promises which extend to mankind in general. We cannot yet foresee what will come of it.

Like every human undertaking, psychotherapy has *its own dangers*. Instead of bringing help to people in distress, it may become a kind of religion, similar to that of the gnostic sects of 1,500 years ago. It may be a substitute for metaphysics and eroticism, for faith and assertiveness, or a substitute outlet for unscrupulous drives. Beneath its apparently high level of aspiration, it may in fact do nothing but reduce the psyche to a uniform and trivial level.

Psychotherapy, however, possesses its own defence against all such risks in so far as it has some understanding of what it knows. The knowledgeable psychotherapist can see through errors very clearly and for that reason is all the more to be blamed should he succumb to them. But only some *established institution* can give formal development and provide rules and regulations which will embody the whole scientific and professional tradition while protecting against these risks.

Gradually we may expect some properly constructed notion of institutional psychotherapy, arising from all that has been learnt in practice. This will rest with those who are actively engaged in it. At this point we can only make a few incidental remarks which may stimulate thought. Aware as we are of the extraordinary possibilities of psychotherapy, we are looking for some clear distinctions. We will not undertake to draw any real picture of what psychotherapy is or has been like in practice but will make a few points from which we might start if we wish to construct a theory of it. In this we shall have to confine ourselves to the most marginal of possibilities, as only the fine point of some extremely simple line of thought can give us a suitable instrument for probing reality as it is.

The basic difficulty is that psychotherapy is a practice which addresses itself to the human being as a whole and the doctor is called on to be more than a physician, so we are furnished with a point of view that is radically different and much more comprehensive than the purely psychopathological one.

(1) *The psychotherapist must understand himself:* In somatically caused illness we cannot require the doctor to do for himself what he does for the patient and prove his art on his own person—a physician may be able to treat a nephritis in his patient with great success and no less well even though he neglects it and mistreats it in himself. In psychic matters, however, the situation is different. The psychotherapist who has not seen through himself can never truly see through his patient because then he allows the assertion of alien, ununderstandable drives within himself. The psychotherapist who cannot help himself can never really help his patient. It is therefore an old demand that the physician should himself be the object of his own psychological scrutiny, and recently this has been resurrected as a primary requisite. Jung formulated it as follows (abbreviated):

The relation between doctor and patient is a personal relationship within the impersonal framework of medical treatment . . . treatment is the product of reciprocal influences . . . an encounter takes place between two people who bring with them a vaguely defined sphere of unawareness as well as what is possibly a state of clear, full consciousness . . . if any contact is made, both parties will be changed . . . the patient influences the doctor unwittingly and brings changes about in the doctor's unconscious . . . effects which we cannot formulate better than in the terms of the old idea of transferring the illness on to someone healthy, whose own good health has to drive the demon of illness into submission . . . in acknowledgement of these facts even Freud accepted my *demand that the physician should himself be analysed.* This means that the doctor is just as much in analysis as the patient . . . analytical psychology therefore requires an *application to the doctor himself* of the *system he has for the time accepted* and he must do this with the same ruthlessness and tenacity as he shows towards the patient . . . it is not popular to demand that the doctor has to suffer change in order to be able to modify the patient, first because this seems impracticable, secondly because preoccupation with oneself is subject to prejudice and thirdly because at times it is painful to find in oneself all that one expects to find in one's patients . . . the most recent developments of analytical psychology put the doctor's personality into the foreground either as a therapeutic factor or the opposite . . . the doctor is no longer allowed to escape from his own difficulties by treating those of others . . .

From this viewpoint has evolved the *demand for a training analysis.* No one who has not been relentlessly analysed for 100 to 150 hours a year by the methods of depth-psychology is thought fit to take part in expert discussions in psychology nor to practise psychotherapy. 'We do not want to learn on patients but on ourselves. We do not want to uncover the most vital things and deal with them before we have to a certain extent understood and seen through ourselves. We owe this to our patients.' Hence the training analysis is intended to become an essential part of the training of future psychotherapists. There is unusual insistence on this demand, although there are leading psychotherapists who have not, so far as we know, allowed any analysis of themselves by methods of depth-psychology. In this regard certain matters need to be kept clear:

(*a*) *There is a valid and unavoidable demand for self-illumination:* The only question is *how can this be achieved* and whether the direct help of someone else is necessary, someone who will lay bare the psychic recesses for a professional fee. Self-revelation should not be confused with an inter-personal method of analysis. We cannot secure what Existence itself must foster. Nor can we control or attest to intra-psychic events which always remain unique and unrepeatable. It is, therefore, worth considering whether the demand for self-illumination should be denied the widest possible play of choice for its realization. The individual should be able to choose whether he will entrust himself to someone else for analysis or whether he will be indirectly stimulated by personal contact or whether in the course of his life he will link himself with the great illuminating experiences of history (e.g. Kierkegaard's 'Sickness unto Death') and receive his own personal revelations, or whether he will do all of this together. If what is innermost to one is turned into something that can be externally controlled and the preconception upheld that among accredited psychotherapists there are always some to be found to whom any young adult could reveal and entrust himself unreservedly, it may well be that exceptional persons will be deterred from such a profession, and possibly just those who are the most indispensable, humane and soundest among them, and best able to advance psychotherapy further in research and practice. The founders of institutional psychotherapeutic training must ask themselves (liberating their own desire for illumination from the confusions of their own school) whether the demand for a training analysis does not sometimes hide something like a demand for a declaration of faith and the vindication of something that pertains more to the preservation of a sect than to a public form of therapy. They should also ask themselves whether the true idea of constant self-illumination as necessary for the psychotherapist is not in the end a misunderstanding when there is a fixation upon one particular form of exploration, which wavers between an analysis, with the therapist impersonally present in the background, and a personal communication face-to-face. It would be a confirmation of my own suspicions if there should be a demand for training analyses according to the different psychotherapeutic schools and a separation of one from the other so that the prospective student would have to make his choice. A truce would have to be called as between warring religions, whereby each secretly hopes that in the end it will prevail as the only, true one. Should this happen it would clearly expose the philosophical character of the required training analysis and how it was in fact a substitute for the movements of religious faith.

In psychotherapy a deceptive path leads us into the confines of private philosophies and to avoid this we have to drop, not the training analysis, but the training analysis as an indispensable condition for training in psychotherapy. The only unconditional requirement is that the psychotherapist should illuminate himself, but this should not be subjected to any objective control, examination or assessment, by others. The content of the established institutional training would have to be what is accessible to all and objectively valid, although in practice everything decisive will depend on the personalities who make use of what they have been taught.

Every profession needs the protection of a well-defined tradition. A young profession in process of establishing itself may have unrestricted possibilities but it may become limited by the choice of its initial organization. To choose a training analysis as an arbitrary criterion for admission to the profession would lead to the restrictedness of several mutually exclusive and opportunistically tolerant schools and finally to the extinction of the profession itself. The individual needs a lifetime to found himself successfully upon that traditional practical wisdom of mankind from Plato to Nietzsche, which is the characteristic feature of psychotherapy as distinct from medical therapy in the narrower sense. Or to put it differently: Every intellectual movement is materially determined by the men who founded it. Winkelmann set the level for archaeology which obtains to this day though most of his theses have had to be abandoned. His natural distinction and the depth of his ideas all left their mark. But in regard to psychotherapy we must not be deceived, no movement of this high order could ever be based on Freud, Adler and Jung and because one grows dependent on one's opponent, no successful engagement with them along their own lines will ever find the way. This can only come by our getting a grasp on the great traditional truths. It would be well for present-day experience to recognize these truths and appropriate them to psychotherapeutic practice in which therapists are now completing the foundations for the future in a situation of transition. They are being called on to create a body of teaching which can be accepted and which so far does not exist. There can be no final appeal to experience nor to a number of personality-types that call for their own particular methods. Creative understanding, that glimpses and demonstrates what is true, simply collapses among vague simplifications of this sort. Once truth has been grasped from the depths of our tradition and concretized in contemporary form, we should automatically recognize the valuable, inadequate, accidental and destructive elements in the older authors who today still influence to a large extent, either anonymously or overtly, the psychotherapy which they themselves have set in motion.

(*b*) We have to draw a distinction between *a depth-psychology which illumines* and a *psychological technique.* Depth-psychology as practised implies an involvement with contents and viewpoints, the experience of which influences the whole outlook of the individual and acts by unconscious suggestion however aware the individual is. The actual undergoing of the therapy already implies an acceptance. Psychological techniques on the other hand which are used therapeutically (hypnosis, autogenic training, exercises, etc.) bring a specific set of experiences gained through the use of a new instrument. It is fair to ask that psychological techniques which we want to use on someone else should first be tried out on ourselves with the help of experts. But where techniques are set aside in favour of direct and personal contact, the meaning of which can never be arbitrarily contrived and which therefore no amount of methodical reflection can turn into a technique, we must be careful not to confuse the two. Success depends on our confronting the unconscious depths with an enhanced respect. We have to avoid turning everything into a technique if we are to keep open communication with our own nature. We must not expect that the personal qualities of the psychotherapist will spring from formal instruction; the professional demands are much more far-reaching and among them there is something essential that most decisively cannot be taught.

(2) *Healthy and neurotic people:* In the passage quoted above on the need for the physician to apply the analysis to himself Jung continues:

The self-criticism and self-exploration inseparably linked with this question call for a concept of the psyche quite different from the purely biological concept that has been in use up to the present because the human psyche ... not only entails the patient but also the doctor ... not only the object but also the subject ... what before was a method of medical therapy now has become a method of self-education ... *here analytical psychology breaks the bonds* which hitherto confined it to the doctor's consulting-room. It fills the wide gap which hitherto placed the occidental cultures at a psychic disadvantage to those of the orient. We only recognized psychic submission and constraint . . . When a psychology which is primarily medical takes the doctor himself as its object, *it is no longer just a method of treatment for patients*; it now deals with those who are healthy and who can only be said to be ill in the sense that all men suffer.

Jung clearly formulated something that had been happening all along. But what might have been considered a weakness or a fault in therapy, was turned by him into a strength and a function of it. It is all the more urgent for us, therefore, to bear in mind a few fundamental distinctions:

(*a*) *The difference between neurosis and health:* Only a minority of people are neurotic, the majority are healthy. There is *an essential difference* between neurotic phenomena and the healthy psychic life which all can share. The majority of people have no experience of neurotic phenomena and therefore do not understand these phenomena at all.

There are *transitions* between neurosis and health in so far as a minority of healthy people can show neurotic phenomena, usually in episodic form. This does not mean that all people are a little neurotic but only that isolated, transient phenomena may appear in otherwise healthy persons. It also means that only a small minority of people will be affected by sporadic, neurotic phenomena; the majority know nothing about such things whatsoever, and the few who do can be regarded as on the whole healthy persons at that.

Though there cannot be any serious doubt over these views, the last may perhaps be questioned. Neurotic phenomena are the *consequences* of psychic difficulties which every healthy person knows and overcomes. Existential psychological situations of 'anguish' belong to humanity in general and are not neurotic manifestations. We cannot deny that in the majority of neuroses the universal difficulties of life play an essential part but failure to stand up to the stresses of life through lack of self-understanding, through dishonesty, self-deception, and poor-quality behaviour tends to produce inferior character rather than neurosis. Neurotics are different from these countless, existentially deteriorating but healthy people, as there is also a difference between base behaviour and illness. Before neurosis can be said to arise, something decisive and specific for neurosis must be added: there must be a definite disposition of the psychic mechanisms. It is these alone which permit neurosis to arise from some failure to meet the urgency of the life-situation. Neurosis is thus possible even where there is self-understanding and integrity. We can sometimes say of a neurotic person: 'his neurosis deserves respect'. Given the mechanisms, neurotic phenomena can appear not only through craven refusal but through the actual seriousness of the upward struggle.

(b) *The distinction between therapy and assistance in psychic distress:* Everyone needs self-illumination and self-reassurance through his inner activity. We all need to master life's problems, renounce and refuse as well as accept the reality of life as it is given. The neurotic minority alone need therapy. Coping with life's difficulties, maturing, fulfilling one's existence means one thing, the curing of neurosis another. Correspondingly there is a difference between helping psychic stress and medical therapy.

Every healthy person has the task of finding a way out of life's problems, of taking up some attitude towards himself and educating himself. If the problems are great, some other person—a psychotherapist perhaps—may well be able to throw some light upon them. But neurotic phenomena require special medical measures for their cure, although within the framework of these general human help can be invaluable in a rather unforeseeable way. With certain neurotic phenomena the process of becoming oneself is also a means to cure the neurosis. Depth-psychology at its limits coincides with the illumination of Existence itself and calls for personal closeness and friendship of a unique and contemporary character. Within medical confines psychotherapy becomes on the contrary an application of techniques that can be described, it remains impersonal and can be repeatedly applied and taught.

Between people everywhere communication is possible which cannot be scientifically or medically contrived and in which self-fulfilment comes about through a revelation of the person, but in relation to neurosis in the psychotherapeutic sense there is both more and less to do. There is less existential communication (however pleasant and helpful such communication may be for the neurotic and however much he needs it should he recover), because such communication cannot take place according to plan, intentionally or professionally. But there is more than existential communication, in so far as psychotherapy is the application of an expert technique, and measures, tested by experience, are taking specific effect.

This has relevance for the answer to a practical question. It would be grotesque to ask a fee for providing existential communication. Fees only make sense where there is the offer of technical services which depend on a definite body of knowledge, a teachable expertise that can be applied universally and repeated. But as in all medical therapy we find on occasion the unintentional beginnings of existential communication between doctor and patient so it is when we come to psychotherapy. Communication of this order is something additional which can neither be sought nor given in return for money. But we cannot turn into a therapeutic principle or purpose everything that may happen in the course of depth-analysis or during that illumination of Existence when two people are face to face. Such communication is possible in all human relationships and where they are genuine and fateful, it will support and further them but in respect to itself it stands beyond the human world of give-and-take.

(c) *Universalization of psychotherapy:* None of the above distinctions prevent psychotherapy being offered to all people who, for instance, have difficulties with their work or who cannot solve their domestic or family misunderstandings, or who are baffled by problems of educating their children. Even healthy people find complications for which a resolution needs to be found. Methodical knowledge and technical ability in the hands of some able person may be of help even where there are no psychopathological phenomena and such help may be more successful and lasting than in the case of neurosis itself. Sensible counsel at the right moment can do wonders and attainment of insight makes scales fall from the eyes of some people, even so do counsellors who act within some institutional setting achieve success. The possibilities here cannot be foretold.

This constitutes a step from medical psychotherapy to a concern for the problems of healthy people so far as they can be helped psychologically. In the long run therefore it is all the more necessary to be clear what these activities mean. There is a common phrase which suggests that healthy people at present are not inclined to submit themselves to help of this sort; when someone has rejected our offer of help we say: we could treat him if only he had some symptom or other (i.e. some neurotic manifestation).

We obscure the whole idea of psychotherapy if we adopt the attitude: psychotherapy is necessary for everyone and not only a solution of specific stress; the stresses involved are shared by all mankind. Such a view goes beyond all measure. Every person helps himself through communication with his closest and dearest and through such faith as he can muster from what the world offers him. He only takes the step of turning to some stranger, paying him a fee and revealing himself without that reserve which only stress breaks down, when he is in dire distress, lacking perhaps any true relationship, having fallen out with his environment or lost faith in an empty world. We have not yet solved the problem of how help of this sort can be organized if the distinction between medical psychotherapy and general psychological counselling is to be preserved, that is, whether we should foster the tendency to universalize psychotherapy into a general form of psychological guidance or whether in the end new limitations should be set confining psychotherapy to the neuroses and presupposing a judgment of 'ill-health'.

(3) *The personality of the psychotherapist:* A great deal is expected of a psychotherapist; superior wisdom, unshakable kindness, ineradicable optimism, he is supposed to contain them all. Ideally, it requires a life-long self-scrutiny by someone rich in experience if humility is to be ensured by a proper knowledge of human limits and one's own limitations. As soon as psychotherapy has become organized into a profession through the provision of theory and training, how can opportunities be created for *exceptional personalities* to take their own line of action? Training, selection, control create defences against unsuitable persons, and this is all the more necessary as it is still a growing profession, not yet consolidated by any time-honoured tradition; it will therefore be invaded by many disturbed, neurotic and curious people.

(a) *Creating standards:* If there is a future for psychotherapy, there will one day be a human representation of how it can be done to perfection. The personal factor plays a central role in psychotherapy in a very specific way but the right person has not yet arrived. But even the best of prototypes would have his own particular limits and lacks and could not be wholly imitated. He could only offer some orientation and encouragement for his successors. While we are without any public example of such a prototype whose life could be reviewed, we can only discuss in abstract fashion what we might expect. We have selected a few examples from the usual cultural and ethical requirements:

Opposition to sectarianism: Psychotherapy rests on faith but does not create a faith. If the therapist is to preserve his integrity he must be able to accept real faith openly and positively; he must also resist the tendency (which experience shows is unavoidable) to turn psychotherapy into some philosophical system and convert the circle of psychotherapists, pupils and patients into a sect.

I once asked a doctor whether it would perhaps be advisable to call in a psychotherapist for an hysterical patient and he answered: 'No, she is a practising christian.' Such an absolute alternative is of course not wholly valid but it has some application to all that we find of a world-ordering character in various psychotherapeutic writings. Psychotherapy that has become sectarian in character cannot be a representative of any public form of therapy. It will take shape for a time among private circles and then dissolve unless one of the psychotherapists becomes the successful founder of a new religion. We can only counter those sectarian tendencies that lead to groups formed round esoterically admired masters and to psychotherapeutic dogmas by demanding as our standards: clarity regarding the secularization of faith, which is the general tendency of our times; a recognition of the great traditional faiths in so far as they are still alive; the cultivation in oneself of a basic philosophic attitude as the universal medium for knowledge, vision and ability; and clarity over the fact that such attitudes always point to self-recreation in every individual psychotherapist. He has to be a person who can rely on his own resources.

Respect for people: The nature of his experiences and certain necessary psychotherapeutic measures may well induce in the psychotherapist a certain contempt for people. He feels rather like an animal-trainer, lays patients low under hypnosis, drills the uncooperative. He meets with two kinds of situations: first, where there is a plain, commendable readiness to undergo treatment, and neurosis may enhance a person's stature (one can feel love for such neurotics in whom the deeps of existence become manifest), secondly, where neurotic people never become themselves but maintain their life-lie; they do not accept reality and its values but use and misuse them as symbols for something else (in extreme cases they make it possible for one to feel disgust for human beings). The psychotherapist is only kept from a contempt for humanity through the fundamental attitude of wanting to help people as people. He is helped in this by being aware of his own weak points, his own derailments and failures and preserving them in his memory throughout life, but he is also helped by his knowledge of possible success and the liberating and supporting character of fresh encounters. If anyone chooses to be a psychotherapist, he should know of the difficult experiences that await him and be certain of his own love for humanity.

Opposition to therapeutic one-sidedness: There is always a risk of seeing something else in the patient from what one sees in oneself. The therapist goes to work on the patient as if he were some natural object of little concern to himself. But psychologically speaking man finds himself in the other. It is only then that he can help with all that is within him. The psychotherapist therefore must make himself the object of his own psychology to the same extent and degree of depth as he expects from his patient.

(b) *Acceptance of training:* In view of the difficult nature of the profession and the high personal standards required, it is right that access to the practice of psychotherapy should be governed by conditions at least as stringent as those of medicine, so far as teaching, living and practical experience go, nor should psychotherapy ever be separated from medicine. But the demand for medical training cannot be maintained as if it were the only possible basis for helping people in distress. For this, any profession which involves intensive mental work and self-discipline, experience of the world and closeness to other humans will provide equally good foundation. Only mature people can take up psychotherapy of this character. That the somatic therapy of neurosis should remain in the hands of physicians is just as much a matter of course as that they should invite non-medical people in as auxiliaries and that where the application of psychotherapy is extended to healthy persons, even non-medical people achieve increasing importance.

(c) *Training:* Apart from the practical experience which has to be directly acquired, there is an important question to be answered regarding what cultural tradition should form the basis of psychotherapeutic studies. It is likely that psychotherapy will only reach any standing if the practitioner returns to the profounder sources of human knowledge, in addition to studying the psychotherapists of the last fifty years, who when all is said and done have confined themselves to the neuroses and are, philosophically speaking, of a lowly order. A human image wants to be gained from an anthropology nurtured on Greek philosophy, on Augustine and Kierkegaard, Kant, Hegel and Nietzsche. At present we have no firm criteria for our cultural and psychological standards. The level is still extemely fluctuating. The human image should only be defined by the greatest of human beings and only they should coin the modes of speech to be used in talking of the psyche. It is from them we can learn to use the concepts which will help the individual to illuminate himself.

(d) *Control:* Institutions or organizations can only exercise a superficial control in order to eliminate the unsuitable in due course and make it more difficult for the psychotherapist to make mistakes.

(1) By offering a number of opportunities the institution may usefully resist levelling-down through mutual agreement and the tendency to dissipate into individual efforts. It should offer possibilities for solitude which is the source of all quality, by giving the individual the freest possible range for his initiative; validation must take place in meaningful exchanges between psychotherapists, they should see themselves in the light of their own work (so far as this can be seen), converse with each other and freely discuss scientific publications, they should invite criticisms of these and of themselves and impose no limits to this.

(2) Because of its intimacy psychotherapy brings certain risks which no-one knows better than the psychotherapist himself. There are occasional rumours of individual lapses and occasionally they are true. But they are sufficient to call for the requirement that should a psychotherapist develop an erotic relationship with his

patient of a sexual character, even if it were only once, he should desist from psychotherapy.

A further requirement could be that a psychotherapist should be married if he or she treats persons of the opposite sex. The average, secularized psychotherapist can hardly have the rigorous standards expected from a catholic priest, supported by the tenets of his faith. But such a requirement seems to offer too naïve a solution. Marriage gives no guarantee of good behaviour and the unmarried can be beyond reproach. The required psychic level of the pyschotherapist cannot be determined by the mere fact of his marriage, although the latter may well enhance it.

This particular problem is touched on rather than discussed in the psychotherapeutic theories of 'transference'. The psychotherapist as a person cannot help but play a decisive part in the psychic processes of the patient. What has to be done is to combine this *personal function* with *impassible distance* so that objectivity is preserved and in the course of the unavoidable, unique indiscretion of the revelations of depth-psychology personal factors in the psychotherapist are successfully excluded. Within the personal factor something impersonal must be operative. Even social contact between psychotherapist and patient is already a mistake, and what relationship there is must be limited to the psychotherapeutic contact. But if this distance cannot be achieved, the risks are obvious. Once an element of desire and mutual private attachment enters into the ordinary respect for the person who carries out psychic counsel and cure, in principle the situation is ruined. Should it ever be thought that the erotic links between patient and psychotherapist and the erotic satisfaction of the one by the other were the main factors in cure (in current phraseology—provide the most effective transference and means for its solution), psychotherapy would have become little else than skilful seduction. The historical study of the gnostic sects reveals the unending metamorphoses which the role of the therapist can assume, in the guise of physician, saviour or lover.

INDEX

Adler, Alfred, 25, 40
Aporia, 16

Body-psyche unity, 1, 16–17

Charcot, Jean Martin, 9
Communication, doctor-patient, 14–
20, 25–28, 39, 41, 43–45
Confessions, use in psychotherapy,
2, 10, 36
Crime, responsibility of patients,
12–14
Cure
limits of, 23
meaning of, 23, 25–27
symbols used in, 6, 10, 33
wholesale, 9, 29

Depth-psychology, 17, 20, 38, 41,
43, 49
Doctor
authority of, 1, 3, 6, 16–17, 21, 27
judgment of, 2, 8, 10, 32
knowledge of, 8–9, 11, 17, 30,
47–48
as limiting element in relationship,
15–18, 45
personal psychology of, 27–28, 37–
38, 47–49
as priest, 6, 10, 29–30, 46, 49
self-illumination of, 38–40
view of patient by, 17–18, 37, 46–
49
Doctor-patient relationship, 1, 6, 15,
18, 37–39, 43–44

Environment
change of, 3, 5
loss of contact with, 45
social conditions forming, 10–11
Existence, 18–20, 38, 43

Faith, religious, 1, 10, 23–24, 29,
33–36, 46
Freud, Sigmund, 2, 25, 28–29, 38,
40

Goals, psychotherapeutic, 6, 11, 23–
26
God, 23, 25, 33–34; see also Faith
Göring, M. H., 35

Health
definition of, 12, 23
as goal of therapy, 41, 45
Hegel, G. W. F., 48
Hypnosis
suggestion in, 1, 6
as a therapeutic technique, 17, 22,
41

Illness, physical, 1, 27
Institution
as a change of environment, 3, 5–6
as control of psychotherapist, 48
place of law in, 9–10
as a world, 34–37

Jung, C. G., 37, 40–42

Kant, Immanuel, 48
Kierkegaard, Sören Aabye, 39, 48

Laws, affecting patient's freedom,
12–14
Life-lie, maintenance of, 23, 27, 47
Life-situation, 5–6, 43; see also In-
stitution
Loyola, Ignatius, 29

Nietzsche, F. W., 21, 27, 29, 32,
40, 48

Patient
as biological event, 20

freedom of, 20, 22
free-will of, 12–13
illness as object, 15
judgment of, 4, 10
physical exercises for, 2–4, 22, 41
regimentation of, 3, 5
right to know, 16
self-illumination of, 2–5, 18–22, 33, 43; see also Communication
self-relaxation of, 3, 23–24
submission to doctor by, 1–2, 4, 16–17, 28
training of, 3–4, 20–21, 41, 46
will-power of, 4
Prinzhorn, Hans, 25

Psyche, 1–3, 5, 15, 18–20, 21, 33, 41
Psychotherapy
aim, 25
development of, 34–36
Psychiatrists, 7, 19, 27–32, 46

Religion; see Faith; God

Schultz, J. H., 3, 23–24
Science, limitations of pure, 5–8, 11–13, 20, 24, 31–32

Weizsächer, V. von, 9, 24–25, 27–28

Yoga, 24, 29